every
breath
i take

every
breath
i take

Surviving and Thriving
with Cystic Fibrosis

Claire Wineland

with

Chynna Bracha Levin

BusinessGhost Books
Irvine, CA

Business Ghost Books
www.businessghost.com

ISBN: 978-0-9836406-7-7

Printed in the United States of America

Cover Design: Leo Cadiz
Book Design: Dotti Albertine

This book is dedicated to Vanessa.
She was my first friend with cystic fibrosis.
She passed away in 2008 yet
I still think of her all the time.
She was a brave fighter!

–Claire–

For my mother, Suzanne Levin,
who has given me love my whole life,
and for my grandmother, Jenny Graubart,
now celebrating two generations of dedications.

–Chynna–

contents

acknowledgments 9

Chapter 1 growing **up** as a CF kid 11

Chapter 2 the **surgery** 21

Chapter 3 the **coma** 27

Chapter 4 the **aftermath** 35

Chapter 5 the **foundation** 43

Chapter 6 life **goes** on 55

support families 68

acknowledgments

i would like to acknowledge my teachers; my friends who are there for me whenever I need them; and my family, always there for love and support. I would like to acknowledge Claire Wineland for her courage and openness and for giving me all the information that we put into this book. Special thanks to my father, Michael Levin, for helping make this book a reality. Thank you to my brothers Walter and Isaac and my sister Aliya for all your love.
— **Chynna Levin**

my gratitude goes to Miller Children's Hospital/ Memorial Care Long Beach, CA; Drs. Nussbaum and Randhawa; the pediatric ICU doctors; and all the excellent caregivers in the Cystic Fibrosis Clinic at Miller Children's Hospital; Claire's Place Foundation and all the people who

acknowledgments

support us in this endeavor to help others surviving and thriving with cystic fibrosis.

— Claire Wineland

we both wish to acknowledge Meghan Heritage, who made this book a reality; the beautiful interior design and layout by Dotti Albertine of Albertine Book Design; and Leo Cadiz, who created our awesome cover design!

— Chynna and Claire

Chapter 1

⟶

growing up as a CF kid

"**Cystic fibrosis** (also known as CF or mucoviscidosis) is an autosomal recessive genetic disorder affecting most critically the lungs, and also the pancreas, liver, and intestine. It is characterized by abnormal transport of chloride and sodium across an epithelium, leading to thick, viscous secretions."

—*Wikipedia* Definition

the definition above seems like a lot of big words for something that has been a part of my life since I was born. I'm a CF kid, and the disease has been a large piece of shaping who I am, especially over the last two years, but all the long medical terms don't really help explain what it's like to live with cystic fibrosis. I'm not sure if I can do much better, but I'd like to give it a shot. I'll try to talk about things as simply as possible, but that's one of the first things to learn about living with CF—nothing is ever really simple.

Cystic Fibrosis—The Medical Facts

cystic fibrosis is a genetic disease, so both of my parents had to be carriers in order for me to be born with it. That doesn't mean that they have the disease; just that the defective gene that causes it is in their DNA. CF isn't always detected when you're first born. In fact, a lot of CF kids are misdiagnosed with things like asthma or stomach disorders before doctors can catch the CF. However, I was born with a meconium ileus, which is a giant cyst in my stomach, so it was obvious right away that my life was going to be very different from what most kids would consider "normal."

Cystic fibrosis is also a progressive disease, which means it gets worse as time goes by. Basically, what happens is that the disorder causes a sodium deficiency in your body that then causes an overload of mucus that builds up in your lungs, sinuses, stomach, pancreas, and pretty much anywhere else mucus might gather.

Over time the mucus starts to gather everywhere and can cause different problems for different organs. In the pancreas it prevents insulin from being released, which gives you Type

One diabetes, or CF related diabetes. It can also prevent your pancreas from releasing enzymes so you can't digest food, or it can fill your stomach with mucus, making you constantly nauseous. When you're diagnosed with CF, you learn you have a specific type—mine is Delta F508 Delete, which is another really long word that basically means my CF affects both my lungs and gastro-intestinal system.

No matter what variation of cystic fibrosis you have, infections, viruses, and bacteria are eventually drawn to all of the built up mucus, and they don't want to leave because the mucus forms little pockets around itself. Your body tries to isolate those pockets by surrounding them with other pockets in the airways, but *those* pockets just trap more mucus, more bacteria arrives, and the whole process starts over again. Eventually the pockets will start to fill up with scar tissue, which starts to clamp off parts of the lungs. Right now, my upper right lobe and lower left lobe are closed off and pretty much don't work.

That's the big concern with CF—mucus drawing infections, pockets and scar tissue forming, and organs shutting down—but the basic pattern can affect a person's body in many different ways—ways you would never think would be related to CF. For example, very few women suffering from CF can have children because the mucus can affect your ovaries. Ultimately, cystic fibrosis is a disease that tests you in so many unusual ways, and not all of them are physical.

Living Together in Isolation *—The CF Community*

although the physical effects of the disease can be tough, having cystic fibrosis is so much more than just dealing with nausea and breathing difficulties. I recently heard someone ask if living with cystic fibrosis was like living with cancer, since both diseases are seen as a death sentence in many cases. However, there are some big differences between the two. First, there is a treatment for cancer. Obviously, it can't always be cured, and sometimes the treatment can be very difficult, but there is something that can be done to help fight it. That isn't the case with CF. Moreover, unlike with cancer, a person is born with CF. While some children may be diagnosed with cancer early in their lives, CF is with you from the moment you are born. You grow up with it and are stuck with it until they find a cure.

The most important difference, though, is that people with cancer can be together.

With a lot of illnesses, it's easy enough to find a community of people who all suffer from it, so at least you have someone to talk to about what you're going through, but CFers can't be together. They just can't. Every day, a normal person comes in contact with all kinds of staff infections, bacteria, and viruses, but their bodies fight off the invaders. With CF, on the other hand, the mucus draws those things in, and CFers can't fight them off.

Because of this, people with cystic fibrosis can't be together. We literally make each other sick. In fact, there used to be CF camps where kids with the disease could go and spend time together, but the government shut them down when doctors figured out that the campers were passing bacteria between themselves, which was making them all sick. Obviously, with all the communication advancements, like the internet, CF kids can now meet and talk without actually coming into contact with each other, but it's still very isolating.

Even though there are counselors to help you deal with living with CF, when you can't actually be with other people who can relate to you, it is really difficult. That sense of isolation runs throughout the CF community, and there have even been many novels written about it, especially romance. It's like the ultimate Romeo and Juliet—you can never date or be together because you will only bring harm to the one you love. Even if you are the most positive and happy person, the kind of person who never lets life get you down, it can be very lonely sometimes.

Because they don't have anyone to relate to, no outlet or communication, many CF kids just give up, and there are a lot of suicides in the CF community. Earlier I talked about the CF camps that were shut down, but now there are actually secret CF camps where some kids go because they just don't care about getting sick. They figure they are going to die anyway, so why not meet with other kids like them.

I think that kind of attitude is the hardest thing for me to deal with because I have fought so hard to stay alive, as have many other CF kids that I've talked with over the internet. We have all fought to get where we are and place such a high value on the lives we have created. I don't know one CFer who doesn't feel the same way—even the kids who are depressed and the ones who take their own lives know how valuable it is.

Because when you have CF, you're never sure how long that life is going to last.

The Hospital—Home Away from Home

a lot of people seem to think that one of the biggest trials of having CF is the large amount of time a CF kid has to spend in the hospital. I can't speak for other CFers, but because I *have* spent so much time there, the hospital feels like a second home to me. Sure, I miss having my freedom and being able to go out, but spending so much time in the hospital has never really been an issue.

It's funny, because I've always been extremely comfortable in the hospital. It's my home away from home, and I feel very safe there—it's the way I've grown up. All of my early memories are of the hospital, but not all of them are of things like procedures and surgeries. Those are certainly a big part of it, but I also remember doing projects with the nurses, having New Year's Eve parties in my room, and spending time with the food service staff cooking in the kitchen.

It's a little embarrassing sometimes to admit all of that when people ask me about it, because the response is always,

"Really? The hospital?" But in the end I can't really care about what people think. This is my life, and the hospital is my home.

Born This Way—
The Reality of Living with CF

the one question that CF kids always seem to get asked is, "What does it feel like?" People want to know if it feels like I'm suffocating, or if I resent other kids for being able to take a deep breath. The truth is, it doesn't feel weird… to me. That's because this is something I've lived with my entire life, and I have no way of knowing what it's like to take a real breath or not have my lungs be partially clamped off.

While I can't speak for all CF kids, I know that most I've talked to feel the same way. We simply don't know what we're missing. There are definitely times when I know I'm feeling something different from what most kids would experience, but instead of being jealous that I can't take a normal breath, I'm actually more curious.

When I was younger and my health was still good enough that I could go to school, every week we would have to run a mile—four laps around the track—in gym class. My teachers knew I had cystic fibrosis, so I didn't have to do the full distance, but I would always try my best to do what I could. Some days I was able to run three laps, others I could only make it around the track twice. Rarely did I make it the whole mile. However, I would see the kids who did run the full mile, and they wouldn't even be that short of breath. Meanwhile, I'd be gasping by the second lap.

I wasn't necessarily envious of the other kids as much as I was curious. I have no clue how that feels; to run that distance and not be short of breath is alien to me. For me, it's the things most people would consider "normal" for a teenager that seem the strangest. People assume I must resent not being able to do a lot of the things most teenagers do, but the truth is that I can't imagine what life would be like if I didn't have to get home at a certain time in order to do treatments.

When others ask me if I want to go to see a movie or go to a sleepover, I have to tell them that, physically, I just can't do it because I have things like oxygen tanks that I need to get home and charge. For me, "normal" is dealing with the limitations of my CF on a daily basis, only they don't really feel like limitations because I don't know any other kind of life.

When I tell people this, their reaction is almost always, "Wow, that must be awful." But it isn't awful; it's just strange. For most teenagers, not getting home on time may land them in trouble, but it's certainly not a life or death issue. For me, it is.

Although most CFers don't know what they're missing, many of us can start to understand that feeling of envy as we grow older. Cystic fibrosis is progressive, so as a CF kid grows up, a lot of times he or she might remember when they were younger and their CF wasn't so bad. As I look back on my childhood, I realize I was a lot healthier when I was seven-years-old than I am now. When you're younger you don't really know what it's like to miss out because you've only had a couple of experiences, but once you get older and start to look back on being younger and healthier, you start to understand that kind of jealousy.

Luckily, some things are starting to change with CF. There still isn't any cure, but the life expectancy of CF kids has increased dramatically even since I was born. Most people diagnosed with CF used to only live until their twenties, with maybe a few bed-ridden thirty-year-olds in the community. Now, however, people with CF are living into their fifties due to advancements in medical research. Still, there is a lot of uncertainty with this disease.

To be honest, however, for much of my life having CF wasn't a big issue. I went to school. I spent time with friends. I didn't look sick. I was as close to "normal" as I could get. Despite having to go through several surgeries and treatments, I had never really felt like the stereotypical CF kid.

Then two years ago something happened that dramatically changed my life.

Chapter 2

the surgery

although I had been living with cystic fibrosis all my life, for most of that time it hadn't really impacted me in any drastic way—I was never the "sick kid." That changed two years ago when I was scheduled to undergo surgery—a fundoplication that would tie off part of my stomach so that I wouldn't have problems with acid reflux. I'd been through the procedure before and, for the first time ever, didn't feel any fear over going into surgery.

My doctor, Dr. Mathis, was one of the best fundoplication doctors in the country and was even planning on doing the surgery laproscopically, so they wouldn't have to cut me open. After a day of recovery, I would be going home. Unfortunately, that's not what ended up happening.

Normally I am very tuned in to how my body feels, and I absolutely hate any kinds of drugs or other things that make me feel loopy or out of it, but on the day of the surgery I was given some "mellow drugs", probably a small dose of morphine and something else, in order to calm me down, even though I didn't really feel like I needed it. After all, I was already pretty calm about the procedure. Because I was given the drugs, though, much of the day is a blur.

One thing I do remember, however, was both of my parents saying they had a funny feeling about the surgery. Although I was a little out of it from the drugs, I reassured them that everything would be fine. I'd been through the procedure before, we had a great doctor, and the surgery was being done laproscopically. I was certain things would go smoothly.

Looking back on that day, I realize there were so many small signs telling us not to go through with the surgery. Not only did my parents have a bad feeling, but an hour before my procedure was scheduled to start Dr. Mathis was called into an emergency surgery and another doctor was brought in to replace him. Although my parents wanted to call off my surgery, I reassured them again. I was used to working with a lot of different doctors, and I knew my replacement surgeon had a good reputation.

So I went through with the surgery, and everything seemed to go well. I woke up and felt fine, but I quickly realized that the surgery had not been done laproscopically. Learning that there had been a change of plans just before my procedure, I found I had stitches and a five inch incision on my stomach. Despite the minor hitch, everything else seemed to have gone smoothly. Although some of the stitches came undone— which should have been a warning sign for us that there was swelling—we were assured that it was all okay. At this point I was so used to surgeries and these kinds of small things going wrong that I didn't even think twice about it. I just figured everything would heal.

The only thing that bothered me was that I had a fever coming out of surgery, and since fevers are normally a sign of infection I was a little concerned. However, my dad told me that everything had gone well, so I figured it would all be fine.

Unfortunately, things didn't turn out fine. Over the next two days my oxygen saturation level continued to go steadily downhill. I was tired all the time—more tired than usual— and I couldn't cough. That was a big concern for me since coughing is how I clear mucus; it's how I stay afloat. However, it wasn't so drastic that we thought something might be seriously wrong, and since no one else seemed especially alarmed, I figured it was all normal.

There was another reason I wasn't too concerned about my downhill turn. During the build-up to the surgery, my doctors had told me that I would have to choose between living with my mom or my dad. Up to that point I had been going back and forth between them, but it had started to get too confusing with all of my medication and treatments. We were starting to have trouble keeping track of which prescriptions had been filled and who was taking me to doctors' appoint-ment. I knew the doctors were right, but it still didn't make the choice any easier.

I love both my parents and didn't want to hurt anyone's feelings, so the night before my surgery I remember saying, "If there is a higher power listening, please give me some kind of sign on which way to go." Then when I started to get sicker after the surgery, there was a lot of talk about me going to stay with my mom, since my dad worked a lot and wouldn't be able to be there with my all the time. Suddenly I couldn't help but think that my downward slide was the sign I had asked for—I would live with my mother and no one would have hurt feelings. I figured that no matter what happened, that was the reason behind everything and that, eventually, I would get better and it would all be okay.

That was when I crashed.

Despite my downhill slide, I was feeling fine until sud-denly, two days after the surgery, my oxygen dropped within five minutes. Ingrid, my old nanny and now a close friend, was with me at the time, along with my Grandmother Edie, and when things started to go wrong she panicked. This is where everything starts to get hard for me to remember, because the oxygen levels in my brain were so low that things around me began to feel incredibly slow.

The last thing I remember before completely cutting out was my mom arriving in the room. It was my dad's day to come, and he wouldn't be there until later that night, but she explained that while she was out driving she suddenly had an overwhelming sense that she needed to come to the hospital to see me. I thought, "Well, that's weird," and then I was out.

Over the next couple of days I flashed in and out of consciousness. They hadn't intubated me yet, and I remember not really being there but not really being anywhere else either. I was in this state where I could hear voices, but it was a lot like it is in the movies—a feeling like I was fading in and out and snatching only pieces of conversations here and there.

At one point I came to and knew there was something really wrong. I thought, "Okay, I'm probably going to die now." It seemed completely bizarre to me, because even though I had been very sick for two days, to me it seemed like only a few seconds had passed since I had crashed. I really started to freak out when my carbon dioxide levels went so high that they had to try and intubate me while I was still awake. I was frustrated because I didn't understand what was happening, and for me, as someone who is always so on top of things as far as what medications I'm taking and the technical details of my procedures, not knowing what was going on around me was very frightening.

This was the first time I'd had to let go and trust the doctors, and it was incredibly hard for me. Although I don't have any memories of it, afterwards my family told me that I started to scream and throw things, but all I remember is yelling for someone to talk to me and tell me what was going on.

That's when I went into the coma.

Chapter 3

⚬

the coma

this is the part that a lot of people are interested in, but for me it feels strange to try and explain it because, from my perspective, I was drugged and half dead, living in this weird in-between place where I wasn't sure if what I was experiencing was a hallucination or real life. I was constantly having visions that put me in the middle of strange places and adventures—like being on a sinking boat and having to be wheeled off to an emergency hospital wing in Alaska.

I could still hear the voices in my hospital room, but I couldn't compute what they were saying. I knew there were conversations going on around me, and those conversations worked their way into my visions, translating from medical procedures into surreal adventures. I don't know if it was the drugs or something else, but looking back on it now, I think it might have been a combination of both.

I remember there being doctors. I remember people saying things like, "I'm going to wheel you into this room now." I remember these snippets of scenes in my head, and when I woke up and people explained to me what had been going on while I was in the coma, it seemed to all suddenly make sense.

For example, because I was septic I had developed a very high fever of 105. In order to cool me down, they packed ice around my body; but in my head, in my crazy dream world, I was going through the ice caps in Alaska on a tour with all of my friends and family—everyone was there because I was hearing their voices talking as they worked over me in my hospital room.

In my vision, we were all in Alaska on a big ship, but I kept bumping up against the ice and saying "Ow, can someone steer the ship better? I'm cold!" I had these kinds of crazy scenarios in my head, and when I woke up and people explained to me what had been happening, I realized that the visions were how my mind had processed the events taking place in real life.

Everything started to stick together once I woke up—what my head was doing and what was actually going on. But sometimes there were just voices and sensations, not visions. At one point they had to cut out my port-a-cath but they couldn't put me under anesthesia because my body just couldn't handle it. I remember hearing the doctors talking about it, and finally my main doctor, Dr. Randhawa said to me, "Okay Claire, I've never done this on any other patient, but I believe you can do it. If there is any patient that can come out of it, I think it's you."

I could hear the doctor saying this, but all I could think was, "Come out of what? What are you talking about?" And then suddenly I felt the pain. It was a jabbing pain in my thigh, and I didn't know what it was. I didn't know what they were doing because I couldn't really see them. I could see what my brain was telling me to see, these wacky visions, but I couldn't really see what my doctors were actually doing. I would just feel the pain and think, "Oh my gosh, that hurts," but I wouldn't be able to say anything—I was paralyzed. I couldn't move or talk or scream, but I could hear the things going on.

Through all of this, my doctors were amazing—they became my heroes. It took me a while to relinquish control to them, to be able to say, "I am handing my life over to you," but eventually I felt like I could take that step and let them try to heal me.

I think that was one of the hardest things I had to accept throughout the whole experience—trying to stop struggling and just letting them fix me. There was a point where I finally understood that I had to let go. I could hear everyone around me telling me to relax, to stay calm, and that everything would be okay. At first, all I could think was, "No, it's not okay! I have to fix it!" Finally, though, I accepted it and realized there was nothing I could do. There was something wrong with me, something really not good, but in order to get better I had to hand my life over to someone else and let them do their jobs.

Once I had made that decision, I felt total peace. I didn't have to worry about the outcome. This may sound maudlin, but I thought, "It's okay if I die. I don't have to hold on anymore. I am still going to fight, but I don't have to control it. Whatever is going to happen will happen. I just have to keep doing my best."

It was a very fine line I had crossed, but once I did I felt safe. The entire time it was this balance between, "Ow, it hurts! Make it stop!" and "No, keep going, keep going. Just a little further." I think that was the big struggle for me while I was asleep—not knowing what was going on but trusting that others knew what they were doing and would fix me.

When I finally came out of the coma two weeks later, I was told that I'd had less than a one percent chance of surviving. In fact, they had put me on an oscillator, which is like a high powered ventilator on steroids, and no one with cystic fibrosis has ever come off an oscillator alive. When I look back on that and think about what was actually going on in my head and how my brain was processing all of it, it's such a different experience from what people told me had happened.

Everyone around me was explaining how the doctors were trying to ease me off of the ventilator, but when I go back and try to pick through those memories—the weird visions I had in dreamland—all I can remember is running and knowing that I had to keep going. I was never sure *why* I was running or where I was going, but I had this overwhelming certainty that I just had to keep going. Now it seems strange to hear people talk about how brave I was, because I didn't feel brave at the time. When I was in the coma and experiencing these visions, all I could think was, "Keep going. Keep running."

I had this weird moment the other day while I was watching a National Geographic special about a girl who was in a car accident and had a one percent chance of surviving. At the time, I thought it was really a strange story, but then I remembered that I had gone through the same kind of experience. Sometimes I just don't identify with it, and I have to actually make myself remember that I was the one there, that it wasn't happening to someone else. I was the one that was close to dying. I had to fight to come out of the coma. That wasn't a different person, it was me.

I never thought I'd have to do that, especially when I was in the middle of it. I thought, "I'm never going to forget this, being in my head." And now sometimes it actually takes an effort to remember that all of that happened to *me*. In a sense, it became this part of me that I detached from myself. In some ways that's good, because I don't want to dwell on it, but, on the other hand, I learned so much from the experience. It gave me a completely different perspective on life, and I never want to lose that.

There's always going to be that balance between reliving it over and over again in my mind or totally detaching from it; and neither one of those things is something I want to do. It was an experience that I should remember and take with me, but it's hard to do that without getting fearful and stressed out that it might happen again. That's very challenging.

As I said, the entire experience gave me a new perspective on life. It helped me to realize that we are constantly living on this border between life and death. Something is eventually going to kill you, whether it's a car accident or a plane crash or old age —in fact, you are more likely to die in one of those than of CF. I could just walk out my front door and get hit by an asteroid. We are constantly *this close* to dying, and realizing that creates a different way of thinking, one that is sometimes hard for me to explain to people who haven't gone through it.

Knowing about that border makes it easier to live in the moment. You stop worrying. You stop stressing yourself out about things in the future. As morbid as it sounds, you're not sure what the future could hold—that isn't where you live. You are in the present, and you are always going to be in the present. For me, I look back on how I felt when I was seven-years-old, and I know I'm not as healthy any more.

I could be depressed by that fact, but then I think about four years from now, when the CF will have progressed even more, and I know I will look back on this time in my life and wish for this level of health again, so I need to enjoy it now, in the moment. I can't worry about what happened five years ago or what will come in another five years. I need to be in the present.

When you start looking at life that way it changes the decisions you make. You start feeling safer because you are

You can't get so hung up on where you'd rather be - that you forget to make the most of where you are.

/passenger

able to say, "Right now, I'm alive and I'm doing something amazing and fun. Even through the really rough spots, I know that I'm still alive, and as long as I'm alive I can keep fighting."

For me, this experience was strange because, while I'd had a few near death incidents when I was much younger, they didn't affect me as strongly as this one did. I think that's because I was so young, I hadn't really had a chance to live much of my life yet. When the coma happened I was thirteen and getting ready for high school. I had everything planned out, and then suddenly it all changed. Nothing will go back to what it was like before, and learning to live in the present has helped me realize that's okay. It's freeing, in a sense, because you finally understand that there is a world of possibilities out there if you keep fighting and stay in the present.

As strange as it sounds, CF itself has taught me so many things. I think of life as a toolbox filled with all kinds of "tools"—experiences, talents, and skills—that we collect along the way, and CF has filled my toolbox as full as it can possibly get. Despite what many people think about the disease, I consider that a blessing.

Chapter 4

~

the aftermath

although people sometimes seem to think that talking about my coma and what happened afterwards must be difficult for me, that's not entirely true. It's easy for me to explain the coma, but it's hard for me to go back into the experience, so to speak. If I really concentrate, I can return to that moment. I can smell the smells and feel all of it, and that is slightly scary because being there was so different from my day to day life. Sometimes my mind automatically goes back to that moment, and I have to actually pull myself out of it, but that doesn't mean I can't talk about what happened to me or how it altered my life.

After the coma, my life changed in a lot of ways. Earlier, I talked about growing up with CF and the fact that I never felt like the stereotypical "sick kid." I had a disease, but it was never really obvious.

The coma changed all of that.

I was in the hospital for four months recovering and had oxygen 24/7. I had lost all motor skills during the coma, so I had to learn how to walk and use my arms again. Although I finally got back to a point where I could live a mostly regular life, I was still obviously sick. I looked sick, and I think that was the biggest shock for me and my family. My CF had suddenly become the elephant in the room.

The biggest physical obstacle for me was the loss of my motor skills. Normally, when I'm in the hospital and I want to get out of my room, I just climb out of bed, set my IV pump to an energy saving level, unplug it, and walk down to another ward. At this point, however, my body wasn't my own. I could barely pick up a fork without shaking and throwing it across the room. I wanted to get up, walk around, and be in charge of my health again, but I couldn't.

After I was released from the hospital, I went to live with my mom, just like we had planned when I first started to go downhill before the coma. I know she was nervous. Although she was used to all of my treatments and medications, my medical supplies had suddenly tripled after the coma. Not only did I now have oxygen, but I needed a variety of other medical equipment we had never used before. I had gone my whole life experiencing CF one way and then BAM!, it was a whole different, and much more extreme, story.

For the most part, the entire experience seemed so strange to me because, in my mind, I had only been sick a few days. For everyone else two weeks had passed while I was in the coma, but I felt like things had changed practically overnight, so when I started work on rebuilding everything—especially my motor skills—it was a real eye-opener to see where I actually was health-wise.

I'm the kind of person who always wants to charge full speed ahead, but after the coma I had to stop. I couldn't go, go, go all the time anymore. I had to actually play my part as a sick kid for a while, and that felt weird to me. I wasn't used to dealing with it. My illness hadn't been this prominent thing, and then suddenly it was the center of our lives for a year and a half before things really started to go back to normal.

I'm so lucky to have the most amazing support ever from my friends and family, but, like me, they were used to the old way, when my cystic fibrosis meant limited physical activity but not 24/7 oxygen. When they would come to see me after the coma, they wouldn't say much, but I could see the shock on their faces at actually watching me have to use oxygen and looking and feeling so sick. Everyone was quiet about it; they didn't want to just come out and say, "Wow, you look like crap." They wanted to be nice and supportive about it, but I could tell they saw the difference.

I never went back to school, and I miss that a lot, but my

health just won't allow it. After the coma it was very frustrat-ing because I had moments when I had to remind myself that I was still recovering. I'm used to always being on top of my game, and for the first time that wasn't the case. I was the kid that everyone thought I would be—the sick kid—and my reaction to that was, "No, no, no! I'm not going to let this drag me down." But I didn't have much control over it, over the times when I got healthier or didn't get healthier. That was a huge frustration for me.

However, the physical obstacles weren't the only differ-ences I noticed. I generally try to see things with a glass half full attitude, and I had always been a happy person, but after the coma, for the first time, I felt like I had to work at being happy, where it had once come naturally to me. I had to actu-ally put effort into being positive and okay with things, and that was a whole new experience for me.

As much as I appreciated the coma experience for every-thing I learned from it, I also just wanted things to go back to before, when I could be happy without putting effort into it. I still feel that way—that sometimes I have to work towards feeling positive. I guess everyone does—it's something most people go through at one point or another—but this was the first time I'd had to face that feeling. It was a shock to me to find that I couldn't always be that positive girl in my head anymore.

I actually had to do more visualization and force myself to meditate, which was a big deal for me because it had always come naturally. That's when I started to get a little angry. It wasn't as though I was mad at the world and wanted to run and hide—I was grateful for life and still loved it—but I had these little bits of anger, frustration, and disappointment that I'd never had before. Sure, I'd felt pressure over small things, but I had never experienced the frustration that everyone talks about with teenagers, that attitude of, "I hate life. I hate this world." I had never understood feelings like that, but after the coma I could finally see where they were coming from.

The worst part was that I didn't want to be like that. One of my biggest fears is that I'll become *that girl*—the one that's angry at everyone because she has cystic fibrosis. I've had such a beautiful life because of my CF and the things it has taught me, and I never want to be the angry kid, but after the coma those types of feelings kept coming up. Certain situations would bring them out, and for the first time in my life I started asking myself things like, "Why does it have to be obvious that I'm sick?" or "Why can't people just talk to me about how they feel instead of always trying to be so nice?"

That was another huge problem for me—no one would talk to me about what was going on. I could see that they noticed the changes in me, but everyone was tiptoeing around the subject. It was the same feeling I'd had when I first started to crash—the sense that something was very wrong but that no one was explaining it to me. At the time, what I wanted was for someone to just come out and say, "Claire, you're crashing. You have sepsis, and you may die." It sounds morbid, but I just wanted the truth so that I could accept it in my head. Instead, I had to go blind into everything, and it was the same situation when I came out of the coma.

I've finally come to the point where people can talk to me about the experience and honestly say, "Yeah, you looked really sick," but it took so long for the people in my life to be open with me again and to not feel like they would hurt my feelings or make me depressed if they told me the truth. For example, at one point during my coma the doctors had to actually drain fluid out of my lungs because I was drowning in the liquid. In order to do that they had to flip me upside down, but when they flipped me I swelled up like a balloon because all the liquid went into my tissue. Obviously, I don't remember any of the experience, but I bet it looked pretty bad.

When people would tell me about the coma after I woke up, there was always this two day gap, and no one would talk about what had happened during that time. I'd ask about it, but even my doctors skirted around the details. I've always been able to translate medical talk and know what's going on with my health, and this was different. I was being babied in a way, which I had never felt before because I was always so in charge of everything.

After I finally learned what had happened, I was upset that no one had told me the truth, but now I realize it was because it was so hard for them to see me like that. Now that I'm finally getting stronger, I understand that it's difficult for the people I love to talk to me about these kinds of things because it's not me, it's nothing they've ever experienced with me, and they have no idea how to talk about it.

For my part, I have to accept that this is how things are

going to be from now on. I'm obviously sick. Now I have to learn how to accomplish living with that. Right now, in my life, I've come to a really good point where I'm able to accept the situation and can figure out how to work with people and make them feel comfortable. Although I've learned that sometimes I can't control certain things in my life, I can make the decision to have power over how I live with CF. I can be an advocate, teach people, and give tips on how to live with the disease.

Chapter 5

≫⌒

the foundation

after the coma, things were definitely tough, both physically and emotionally, but something really amazing also came out of the experience—Claire's Place Foundation. Although we have many different resources now, inspiration struck because of one simple fact—it's tough to travel with cystic fibrosis.

An Idea

in a lot of ways, traveling is never easy. You have to pack, deal with planes or other transportation, and sometimes even leave behind the friends and family that help support you.

However, all of that is much more difficult to do when you have CF, or any illness, for that matter.

I love to travel; it's one of my favorite things. For me, it's one of the few "normal" things I have in my life. I'm not saying that I need normal or even want it. I enjoy my crazy, totally abnormal life. But traveling is the one thing I can do that doesn't make me feel like a typical CF kid. When I'm traveling, I'm not the sick kid; I'm just a girl who is traveling. It's the one thing that lets me get away and leave my history behind—rather than dealing with doctors and procedures, I get to have amazing traveling adventures.

However, traveling has never been easy, even when I was younger and didn't have all of the medical equipment I've had to start using since the coma. It isn't just the packing and moving around that's a pain, though. It takes a real effort of strength not to be afraid, to leave behind friends, family, doctors, and hospitals that have been a safety net.

When I'm traveling, it's tough not to think, "What if I start seizing? What if my lungs fail again?" It's very hard emotionally. You're away from the places and people that make you feel safe. That's also part of the thrill of it, though. It's a time when you don't get to rely on hospitals or doctors. You have to rely on yourself, and that can be an amazing feeling.

Back when I was just starting to come out of the coma, I was remembering the strange visions I'd had when I was in that dream world. It was this amazing place with icy glaciers, rolling green mountains, and beautiful crystal coves. It was gorgeous, and I really wanted to go there. When I started to feel well enough, I decided to try and track it down, Googling everything I could remember about the scenery. I found pictures of Alaska and realized it was just what I had seen in my dream.

At the time I didn't think I could travel at all because I needed to have a certain amount of lung function to leave Los Angeles, and I wasn't there yet, but I told my mom about Alaska. She was excited and told me that she had just spoken with my doctor, who had given her the good news—my lung function had increased to the point where I could travel again. Suddenly, going to Alaska was a real possibility. Although I was worried—the nearest hospital would be two hundred miles away—I knew I had to make the trip.

So my mom and I went online and told all of our family and friends. During my coma, so many people learned about my situation and offered their support that we had actually set up a Facebook page so that my parents could update people on my condition, and we ended up with around seven thousand people who were always looking for status updates. It was crazy!

When we posted about the trip, however, all of these new friends started offering things like mileage and condos in the area where we were staying. They donated all of this incredible stuff, which allowed me to take this amazing trip that might not have been possible otherwise.

And that's when I started thinking…

I really wanted to help other CF kids travel. All my life, traveling had been difficult, even more so after the coma. On top of that, a lot of people around me, especially my doctors, would say, "You know, Claire, I don't think you realize how hard it is to travel. I don't want you going. You don't have the right equipment, experience, or support." Because of that, I missed out on a lot of travel experiences.

For example, I'm fifteen and I've never been outside of the United States. It seems so basic, especially in this day and age, but we could never make the trip because, when I travel with my family, we do it all on our own. There's nowhere out there where you can go that might help you with your medical needs when you're traveling.

I knew that if I could change that, I would be satisfied with my life.

I could help other kids travel and learn from my experiences and mistakes—because I've made a lot of mistakes. When I was five-years-old, for example, I flew to Texas to visit my grandparents. It was my first trip alone—my mom was putting me on a plane and my grandparents would pick me up at the other end of my flight. I was so excited, but when the time for one of my treatments arrived during the flight, I couldn't remember what I had done with the bag I needed.

The flight attendant helped me look, but I was freaking out. We finally found it and everything worked out, but ever since then I've been paranoid about losing my stuff. Those are the kinds of things other CF families might want to know about, and I wanted my foundation to give other kids the incredible chances to travel that I had experienced because of the generosity of others.

So when I got back from Alaska I started looking into the possibility of starting the foundation, and it's been such a crazy process since then. Every time I think about it, I can't help but be amazed. "I'm just a teenager!" is the first thing that always comes to mind, followed by, "I don't know how to do any of this foundation stuff." I still don't know how to do any of it—it's over-my-head-adult-stuff. But if I wanted to help kids with CF travel and give them some hope, I had to step up and be that adult.

The Flash Mob

when my parents and I finally made the decision that this was something we definitely wanted to do, we had to figure out how to get the ball rolling and promote our foundation. I remember sitting at the table one day just after I had come home from the hospital. I was weak and not feeling my best, and when my mom came in and told me about this idea her friend had suggested—a flash mob—my first thought was, "What?" At that point, flash mobs weren't very common, and I had no idea what it was. So my mom described it to me, and I figured it would be her project.

Basically, a flash mob is a group of people who learn to do a certain dance and then meet up at a prearranged time and place in order to do that dance in public. The dancers dress like random people in the crowd, so you never really know who's in on it until they've started. The whole thing with a flash mob is that you can't really tell anyone about it, since it's supposed to be this stealth dance routine. Only the dancers and organizers know where and when it is going to be held.

When I finally learned more about it and realized how cool it was, I really started to get excited and wanted to be a part of it. However, in the beginning it was nearly over-whelming. After all, here we were trying to start a foundation while dealing with all of my new medical needs, and now we had to plan a flash mob on top of everything? At first we just weren't sure we could pull it off. We were winging it and figured the whole flash mob idea would be an experimental thing. Before long, though, it turned into this very neat proj-ect, and all of our friends and family, those we told about the idea, wanted to help.

So we put the word out, and suddenly we had twenty people who wanted to choreograph and teach us the dance. Then a friend of a friend who worked as a DJ offered to mix the music for the event, and we chose The Black Eyed Peas' "Pump It" and Lady Gaga's "Born This Way" because both were really fun songs to dance to. Before long, Flash Mob America, an organization that specializes in putting these kinds of events together, contacted us and offered to help. Everything just seemed to fall into place, and before we knew it we were a month away from the event and everything was done. We had actually pulled it off, and we could hardly believe it.

the foundation

It was such an exciting thing to think about. We weren't professionals, but we had managed to put together this amazing event. Not only that, but through planning the flash mob we had actually learned a great deal about our foundation—our goals, ideals, and what we wanted to do—as well as how foundations in general work. Because we had never been in the business world, the flash mob event was our first introduction to something that had never really been our strong suit.

The other important thing for me was to make sure that the event was fun. Fundraisers are usually so stressful, but I wanted this to be something where people could just dance, chill, and have a good time. When we were looking for a location, I really hoped we could snag the Santa Monica Pier, but the legal restrictions involved were just too much. Our next choice was Santa Monica Place Mall, which turned out to be a great decision. Even now, friends tell me that they are having birthday parties there just because it was where we decided to hold this event, so I think we've given the mall a ton of business.

By then, Fox News had learned about my story and had decided to document some of the things I was doing, and around three hundred people—a lot of the same friends and family that had visited me while I was in the coma—wanted to dance. Suddenly our experimental promotional event was something much bigger than we had imagined.

It was all such a neat experience. On the day of the event we performed the routine twice, even though I still wasn't completely healthy after my hospital stay. The first time through was exhausting, and by the end of it I was panting so hard I could barely breathe, but I wanted to do it again. We even had friends who volunteered to film it and create videos—all part of the push to get the word out about the foundation.

Of course, not everything went perfectly. Whenever you put something like this together, especially when television and public attention are involved, there is bound to be some drama as well. Our experience wasn't any different. Although I didn't know the details at the time, I knew something had gone wrong between my parents and one of the groups helping us, and it was hard to watch because suddenly this amazing event had a shadow hovering over it. It was even a while before we could use our own footage from the event, which was really disheartening since that was our entire plan for promoting the foundation in the first place.

Because of that experience, there was definitely a lot of negativity during a time that should have been a huge victory celebration, but then my parents and I started to realize that things like this come up when you have a foundation and are working with other people—it's not always going to be fluffy and happy. However, what really counts is how you handle things when it gets rough—and it definitely got rough for us for a while. Although it was all eventually sorted out, there have been a few other times since then when similar incidents have happened, and it always makes me wonder how people can do things like that. Our foundation is nonprofit. We're not trying to take anyone's money, and we're not trying to be corporate, yet some people want to make it into that.

The entire situation tested all of us, especially in how we handled the bigwigs and their offers to give us money in exchange for doing things a certain way. Sure, it would mean more funds for the foundation, but if it compromised what we were trying to do then was it really worth it?

It wasn't.

To be honest, I had no clue how big our foundation would get. However, it's definitely growing, and that can be a little scary. I don't know what's going to come of it, and sometimes other people don't have the best intentions. Being a fifteen-year-old in the business world is weird, and it can put me in the tough position of having to be an adult and saying, "No, this doesn't feel right. I don't want to make a deal with these people because it goes against my morals." It takes a lot to be able to stand up and say that, but if something doesn't go along with what you believe, you have to say no. There is no compromising.

And, honestly, all of this makes life a little strange. When my friends call and ask if I want to go to the mall or the movies, I sometimes have to say, "I can't. I have a business meeting." It makes me feel so mature, but not necessarily in a good way, more like I've missed my teenage years—even though I know I'm only fifteen and still have many more teenage years to go. It can be hard to find a balance between everything, because I am so passionate about the foundation, but I also don't want to be an adult who wishes I had enjoyed my childhood more. I don't want to have any regrets.

Moving Forward

the smaller moments of negativity aside, the foundation has been an amazing thing in my life, and the response we've received from other people around the world has been fantastic. Much like the flash mob event, the foundation has grown into something so much bigger than anything I could have imagined.

Cystic fibrosis is the number one genetic illness in the world, but there is no government funding for it. Because of that, all of the donations made usually go to finding a cure, which is great, but it doesn't really help families and kids living with the disease here and now.

Because of this, our foundation has started to take on a lot of different roles. We have the CFU—Cystic Fibrosis University—to help kids and families learn how to live with CF. We have tips and tricks on everything from how to deal with mean nurses to how to handle certain procedures and surgeries to things you can do when you get bored in the hospital, all the parts of coping with daily life.

We also have funds for families that have been in the hospital longer than twenty-one days. When your child is dealing with CF, you are bound to end up in the Pediatric Intensive Care Unit (PICU) at least once, and usually for a long period of time, like when I went into my coma. I was really lucky, because, through my Facebook page, I had several thousand people around the world who were praying for me and sending my family money to help support us.

the foundation

Unfortunately, very few children have that level of help. As a result, parents can spend months at a time trying to be with their seriously ill child, but they still need to go to work and pay the bills. How can they do that, though, when they're sitting at someone's bed side?

I really wanted to find a way to support families in that kind of a situation. The funny thing is that my mom and dad felt the same way. In fact, they were really passionate about it because they were coming from a parents' perspective. They knew what it was like to be worried about a sick child while also trying to pay the bills. Because we all felt this way, we started collecting donations to help fund just those kinds of families, a way of helping them make their car or house payments for a few months so that they could focus on helping and supporting their CF kids.

I was so excited to see how many people could actually contribute, and all of the assistance we've received has also helped us start a family support system—matching newly diagnosed families with more experienced CF families over the internet. It's all part of this amazing thing that has developed not only from my coma but from my CF in general.

The most surprising thing to come from all of this, though, is my speaking career—going out to schools and other organizations, including a TED Talk, in order to speak about my experience with CF and the foundation. It's not even a career necessarily, just something I love doing. It helps people everywhere learn about our foundation and what it's like to live with CF.

Sometimes it's insane. I'll be standing on the stage and will have to force myself to remember that this is me. Two years ago I was in a coma, and now I get to do these amazing things, speaking and inspiring people. I get to run a foundation. I am the founder of the foundation! I'm just a teenager, but I have all these crazy, incredible things I get to do with my life, and it's all because I have cystic fibrosis.

Chapter 6

𝄞

life goes on

now what happens? I have friends and family and this amazing foundation, but what, a lot of people ask, what is life like now that I've (mostly) recovered from the coma?

Friends

well, I have a phone for the first time in my life, so I've finally started texting. I'm a very social person, and I love spending time with my friends, so texting is just one more way I can keep in touch with them since I'm not in school on a daily basis.

Actually, I'm very lucky to have those amazing friends, ones who have supported me throughout the coma and CF in general. When I was younger, I remember all of my friends digging the fact that I had CF and accepting it. We even made up games around my treatments. For example, one of my treatment masks looks like a fish face, and when I was little we used to put the mask on and pretend to be fish while I went through my treatments. They made it fun for me, setting up sleepovers in the hospital when I had an extended stay and always making sure to be there when I came out of surgery.

Because I have such amazing friends, I didn't realize until I was older that most kids with disabilities aren't as accepted as I am. Many of them are mocked and bullied, which is shocking to me because I have always had so much support. However, there are tons of kids who commit suicide because they don't have that same encouragement. When I'm with my friends, we sometimes joke around about my CF, but there is never any meanness in it. I've found so much love and support with my friends and family, and knowing there are kids who have to face CF without that kills me.

More than anything, I want to be there for them. However, like I mentioned at the start of this, CFers can't get together, which makes having healthy friends all the more important. When you don't have that kind of support, it's terrible, and you feel even more alone, which is why I want to eventually use the foundation to connect CFers with healthy friends who can give them the encouragement and support they may not be getting from the kids currently in their lives.

It's just one more way the foundation could be used to bring people together.

School

even for me, with the amazing friends I already have, it can be tough to feel like you're in the loop. As I mentioned, I've been home schooled for the last year. I've always been smart when it comes to my medical condition and knowing what's going on with my health, but I've never really felt academically smart because I missed so much school as a kid. I'd be in class for one week and then out for another three in the hospital. It felt like I missed so much during these times, like how to do fractions, and I always seemed to be playing catch-up when I returned to school.

Because of this, I felt pretty stupid by the time I hit eighth grade and went into the coma. I was just so far behind in science, spelling, and reading. I never really expected to do great in school because I have so many other things going on in my life, but I wanted to at least be on the same level as the other kids. Since starting home schooling, I definitely feel like I'm getting a better education, but I really miss actually going to school. I get to see my friends when they visit, but since I'm not in class every day I do feel like I miss out on some things.

I especially don't want to miss out on the high school experience. It's like running a marathon but having to skip the finish line, "I've gone through all of elementary school, and you're really saying that I'm going to miss out on high school *now?*" It seems so strange, because I'm the person schools call to speak at special assemblies in order to teach other kids about life, but I haven't even been to high school! I don't want to miss out on that experience, but I also want an education. I want to be academically smart and caught up for the first time in my life. I'm hoping that when I do go back to school, I won't be the kid who is lagging behind but the one who has excelled.

Sometimes it also feels a little like I'm missing out on the teenager experience in general. Unlike a lot of my friends, I have to prioritize and consider, "Is going to the movies more important than making this video that needed to be finished a month ago?" Making those kinds of decisions is tough as a teenager, because a lot of the time I just want to say, "Forget it, I'm going to the movies." But I can't do that because I have so many bigger plans with my life. It just isn't an option.

For my friends, bigger plans mean college. I have college on my mind, too, but on top of that I also have the foundation, and on top of *that* I have my health. I can't make decisions lightly, and I can't just decide one day that I want to go out and party. Not that I ever had any strong desire to go out drinking and partying—that's never been my thing—but knowing that I don't even have the choice when all of my friends do is strange sometimes.

Then, however, I see all the people I've helped or have moments when I realize how big and important everything we're doing really is.

That's when I know it's worth it.

[handwritten annotation: That is big and important, but having Fon & going to the movies isn't any less big or important (It's just different)]

Why Me?

because my life is so crazy strange, a lot of people ask whether or not I ever wonder, "Why me?" And the truth is… I don't. I know why it's me. I know I have a purpose; I may not know exactly what that purpose is yet, but I am certain that physically and spiritually I have a mission.

Sometimes, however, I wish that I could be a little more oblivious. They say that ignorance is bliss, and to a certain extent I believe that's true. There are kids out there who don't have to worry about the Big Picture, and sometimes I wish I was one of them.

But I also think there are a lot of great things that can come from knowing why you're here and that you're meant to do something bigger. You don't really lose hope or faith as easily when you have that certainty.

As I said, I don't know exactly what my mission is yet. Right now the foundation feels good, but you never know, ten years from now they may cure CF and I'll have a totally different mission. Or maybe my mission is something as small and insignificant as helping someone across the street. Maybe that person will go on to be president and stop a war—all because I helped them across the street. We don't know the chain of events, but I do know that I am here for something bigger and that my CF is a part of that, for better or worse.

Public Speaking

part of that larger mission is something that I stumbled into unexpectedly—public speaking. Giving talks at schools and other organizations has given me the chance to not only spread the word about the foundation but also to tell others my philosophies on life and everything that living with CF has taught me.

Most of the time when people ask me to speak it's about my history, how I got to where I am, and what my advice on life is. However, I was recently asked to speak at a friend's high school on the subject of body image. I couldn't do the talk because I had a big surgery scheduled, but I thought the topic was really interesting.

Being a teenager is rough because there is so much in the media about how kids should look and what their body image should be. Everyone wants to fit that image of perfection, but it just doesn't exist in reality. If I take off my shirt right now, I have a giant scar running straight down my abdomen as well as visible scar tissue in my neck. I also have two scars along my ribs and a G-tube, which helps me get nutrients but looks like an alien probe, sticking out of my stomach.

I don't have "the" stomach or "the" look, so when I was asked to speak I thought it was a great topic. I've spoken before about inner beauty, but this was more about how to deal with being a teen and having scars everywhere. If I'm going to be honest, there are times when all I want to do is wear a bikini, but it really makes people feel uncomfortable.

They stare and ask questions, and although I have no problems with answering those questions, I can tell that people just feel uneasy seeing the scars.

Sometimes I get angry that I can't just be a normal teen, but then I realize that no one is really like that. No one has a perfect body, yet everyone is always so hard on themselves. I should be the last person being hard on myself since the reason I have these scars is because I have survived, but even I get self-conscious sometimes. However, if I didn't have these scars I wouldn't be healthy or even alive, and, in the end, being alive is so much more important than what other kids think of me.

That's become a theme in my life. I speak on many different topics, but this kind of stuff—teenager stuff—is the thing that other teens want to hear about. They want to hear that they are perfect just the way they are. It sounds corny, but I want to be able to tell them that I am not the picture of beauty in any sense, and I'm not very healthy either. Because of that, however, I do not take my health for granted.

I hear about kids cutting their wrists in order to feel pain, or starving themselves, or puking after they eat just to be skinny, and it's like a stab to the chest. I have worked my entire life to be healthy and to treat my body as best I can, but my body is never going to look like the people in the magazines. That's because those people are photoshopped. To hear that kids actually hurt their bodies to look that way is terrible for me. I was born hurt, and I've spent every waking moment trying to be healthier and survive.

Philosophy

i mentioned earlier that I often get asked about my philosophy on life, and if I had to choose just one thing that's been a theme for me, it's that my illness isn't the awful situation most people think it is. I recently learned that in ancient cultures and religions having an illness, or any kind of adversity in your life, was considered a blessing. It was a message from a higher power, an open door filled with opportunity. In fact, the actual translation for "problem" was "empowering situation."

CF, and especially the coma, has been my very own empowering situation. Not only is it the reason for this amazing foundation that has brought people together to help others with the illness, but while I was in the coma there were people in Fiji and Israel who contacted my parents to say they were praying for me. How cool is that? How else but through my CF could I have ever reached so many people?

Alaska was meant to be a chill trip to help me relax after the coma, but it turned into this insane, empowering adventure. I had dinner with a senator and had the chance to ride in a helicopter. I was able to do so many wonderful things that I never thought I would have the opportunity to experience, all because of an illness that most people see as a terrible tragedy.

My entire life has been about helping those people understand how rich having a problem can make your life. There's a saying that I love, "You will never truly get what you want until you want what you have." When I first heard that, I didn't agree. "Wait a minute," I thought, "I don't want what I have! I want more. That's messed up!" But if you think about it, no matter what you have, you're always going to want more. That's human nature.

You may want a bigger house, or more financial security, or a cure, but sit down and ask yourself why you want those things. What about them will make your life so much happier? When you start to think like that, about what you want and the reasons you want it, you begin to see how you can get it with what you have—looking for ways you can make your current situation even more empowering and amazing.

All of this is not to say that dealing with a problem is easy. It is definitely hard, but the thing to remember is that anything you do can be hard. You can make the simplest, happiest thing hard. I've had times when the easiest chore feels like a knife being jabbed at me and other times when it's not tough at all. But, in my life, something being hard and something being bearable are two completely different things.

When my doctor puts me on new meds or changes my treatment schedule, he always asks me, "Is this bearable? Can you handle it? Is this still at your threshold?"

Is it hard? Well, everything has kind of been hard. My life is slightly more of a struggle, at least health-wise, than most other kids. But that doesn't make me want to give up—the question isn't "Is it hard?'. It's "Is it bearable?"

At the moment, yes, it is bearable.

There are certainly times when it's tougher. There are days when I wish I could just not do anything, like that Bruno

Mars song, "The Lazy Song." In fact, one time, when I was having one of those days where absolutely nothing goes right, I was listening to my iPod when that song came on, and I suddenly lost it. I started yelling at my poor iPod, "I can't just not do anything! I never get a lazy day!"

So of course there are days when I wish I didn't have anything to do or days when I just want to be a teenager and not have to worry about adult things, but it's never really been unbearable. I think I'll know when it is, but I'm not there yet. I can bear through the hard days and come out on the other side.

To be honest, I think that giving up—knowing that I could have tried a little harder but didn't—would be much more difficult than making it through my tougher days. Looking at things from that perspective makes me certain that, no matter how hard a day gets, I will keep going.

In fact, one of the messages that run throughout my life is that illness, whether CF or some other disease, doesn't make your life harder. Remember what I said earlier about having one of "those" days, when nothing goes right and you just want to curl up and hide? Well, the truth is that everyone has those days. Having an illness, or any other problem for that matter, does not make things harder. That's just life, and everyone has their own unique set of challenges. If I didn't have CF, I would be a smart, regular girl. I have a loving family, amazing friends, and a beautiful home. I have a good life. For me, CF is my burden, and I have to deal with that.

Handwritten marginalia:

Claire I do want [?] it [or happy?]

"There is never ever going to be a time when life isn't painful. there is never gonna be a time where life is easy and theres no suffering or hardship. - ever

no matter who you are, no matter what you do, no matter where you are in the world, what beautiful things you're experiencing. The pain and the suffering and the despair of

being alive is going to catch up to you — ALWAYS its inevitable.

yeah I'm Sick and I'm dying and I'm in pain alot — at the same time everyone else I've ever known is just as miserable, if not more so miserable than myself.

I think a lot of people use an illness as a scapegoat or as an excuse to feel miserable, but, really, an illness should be an excuse to feel great. It can offer you so many amazing opportunities and benefits that you might not otherwise have.

In fact, when you have an illness or some other challenge in your life, the adversity is not actually the problem. The problem is when you don't know how to handle that adversity, or when you don't know how to handle it gracefully, or, most importantly, when you don't learn from it. The challenge itself isn't the issue; if you can't learn from it and grow from it, that's the real problem.

The hard part... that's just life. The amazing part is how you get through it.

Being able to love what you have, even the challenges, and growing from it is such a gift. The key, though, is not to label things as good or bad. Illness, or any other problem, has always been seen as a negative, but what if it's not? What if it's the exact opposite? What if those people hundreds of years ago in other cultures and religions were right? What if your problem is really this incredible, empowering situation from God?

What if it's your chance to make a difference?

When you stop to think about it, life truly is beautiful. People tend to get discouraged when they have problems to overcome, but, really, that's the part to cherish the most.

That's when you have the chance to get the most out of every second given to you.

...eres just a fundamental quality being miserable like, and I...e never met...yone, who's ok, ...d who doesn't...el a lot of pain.

There is no way of living that can get you out of feeling the kind of despair of being alive, and that can get you out of having to suffer.

Once you let go of that need to rid yourself of things that are uncomfortable, Once your drive behind life isn't based on running away from pain - All of a Sudden you can actually do something of value with your life.

The highs don't mean that you I can respect myself anymore, or that I can be proud of, myself and my life, or that my life is worth living."

So, that's my life with cystic fibrosis. I guess if I wanted to get one message across with this book, it's that I don't want pity. This is my life, and it's pretty incredible. Sure, sometimes I think it might be nice to be a "normal" teenager, but then I wouldn't have had the chance to do any of the fantastic things that have made my life so extraordinary. Anything in life is what you make of it, so no matter what comes your way, cherish it and make something amazing from it.

For more information, contact:
http://clairesplacefoundation.org/

Support Families

Claire's Place Foundation Place Foundation is currently developing a program where families living with cystic fibrosis can communicate with each other and share their experience, strength and hope with newly diagnosed or isolated families looking for support.

Social workers at partnering hospitals will provide families with children with cystic fibrosis information about Claire's Place Foundation, Inc. Families feeling uncertain and isolated will be offered support and information on how to work through the treatment and care process by other parent volunteers. Over the next 5 years, these programs may expand to include actual activities brought to the hospital for children and families to participate in, tool kits, local support groups for families and other groups for youth suffering of cystic fibrosis.

If you are interested in becoming a support family or are in need of a support family to speak with, please send an email to the address below, and we will respond with more information:

melissa@clairesplacefoundation.org

While we build our Support Families Network, please take a look at the following links as a beginning guide to community resources:

Cystic Fibrosis Foundation
Since 1955, the Cystic Fibrosis Foundation has been the driving force behind the pursuit of a cure. Thanks to the dedication and financial backing of our supporters— patients, families and friends, clinicians, researchers, volunteers, individual donors, corporations and staff, we are making a difference.
http://www.cff.org

Cystic Fibrosis Patient Assistance Foundation
Assistance for affording medications and devices for managing CF
http://www.cfpaf.org

Cystic Fibrosis Services
Additional patient assistance programs for those without insurance coverage
https://www.cfservicespharmacy.com/PatientAssistance/

Boomer Esiason Foundation
Links to assistance programs for Tobradex, Creon, Aceon, Estratest HS, Prometrium, EstroGel, Pulmozyme, Advair, and Cipro
http://www.esiason.org/pdf/Cystic.pdf

HospitalBillHelp.org
Guidance for Californians facing hefty hospital bills
http://www.hospitalbillhelp.org

NeedyMeds.org
Additional Patient Assistance Programs
http://www.needymeds.org

Partnership for Prescription Assistance
Database of Patient Assistance Programs
(Search by drug, company or program name)
http://www.pparx.org/prescription_assistance_programs/
list_of_participating_programs

Patient Advocate Foundation
Mediation and arbitration services for patients with
debilitating and life-threatening illnesses.
http://www.patientadvocate.org/

RXAssist Patient Assistance Program Center
Database of Patient Assistance Programs
(Search by drug, company or program name)
http://www.rxassist.org/patients/default.cfm

Life Support Program

Many families are frustrated by the lack of financial assistance that is often desperately needed once their child has been diagnosed with a chronic illness. Many times, only one spouse is working. Sometimes, it is just a single parent without work trying to take care of a sick child. As the bills pile up, parents often feel overwhelmed and can't find anywhere to turn when they can't make ends meet. That is where we hope to provide assistance and help relieve the burden that has become so great for them.

The **Life Support Program of Claire's Place Foundation, Inc.** hopes to bridge the gap and add to the quality of life for the patients as well as the families affected over an extended period of time. Participants can petition the foundation for assistance with long term, or ongoing assistance. The request for assistance process starts by submitting an application and essay along with a referral by their CF center Social Worker, Nurse or Doctor. Financial assistance awards vary based on case-by-case situations. These gifts are designed to help with long term, on-going expenses that will add to the quality of life for the patient and/or the family affected by cystic fibrosis.

If you are interested in applying for assistance through our Life Support Program, please send an email to the address below, and we will respond with more information:

melissa@clairesplacefoundation.org

Extended Hospital Stay Fund

We understand the financial stress that can occur when children with cystic fibrosis have extended stays in the hospital, often in a city far from home. Claire's Place Foundation, Inc. has set up a special cache of funds available to families with children that are experiencing a hospital stay longer than 21 consecutive days.

If you or your family is in this extended stay position, please apply for financial assistance to help with mortgage, rent, utilities or any other basic necessities by asking your hospital social worker to reach out to us by sending an email to us at the address listed below. We will respond with the application and request a letter of referral. The number and amount of assistance will be determined by the board of directors depending on the amount of funds available at the time the application and referral are received.

If you are a child with cystic fibrosis or a family member of a child with cystic fibrosis interested in applying for aid through our Extended Hospital Stay fund, please send an email to the address below, and we will respond with more information:

melissa@clairesplacefoundation.org

You Can Help!
Donate Now!

Printed in Great Britain
by Amazon

34389794R00045